To my husband Shayn who is my rock, and to my boys Jude and Brody who are my sunshine. To my amazing parents Mark and Elisa and all of my family. I hope this book is a good reflection of our beautiful city. In the words of my grandfather who instilled his love for this city in all of his children and grandchildren:

"Pensacola, the western gate to the Sunshine State where thousands live the way millions wish they could, where the warmth of our community comes not only from God's good sunshine, but from the hearts of the people who live here. Welcome to Pensacola, America's first place city and the place where America began."

-Mayor Vince Whibbs, Sr.

Goodnight Pensacola

Copyright© 2015 Anna Whibbs Theriault

PRT0515A
Printed in the United States
Library of Congress Control Number: 2015937837
ISBN-13: 978-1-63177-143-9

www.mascotbooks.com

Goodnight PENSACOLA

Anna Whibbs Theriault

Illustrated by Chiara Civati

As the sun dips low
To welcome the moon
A cross guards a snow-white beach
High above from the dune

A sign welcomes travelers
To swim in gulf waters so blue

The beach ball looms high in the sky
With a 360 degree view

At a trestle in town
Where trains chug above

Nearby drivers can view
Declarations of love

The Blue Angels zoom by
In a formation so tight
Over the Blue Wahoos stadium
Whose cheers will soon fill the night

The locals paddle hard
To catch the last set of the day

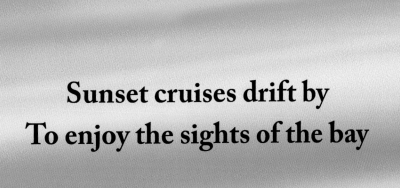

Sunset cruises drift by
To enjoy the sights of the bay

Lines are cast from the pier
To lure the colorful fish swimming by

Lifeguards keep silent watch
From their towers up high

Ft. Pickens echoes the story
Of times long ago

As the sun finally sets
On the beautiful town down below

Goodnight Pensacola

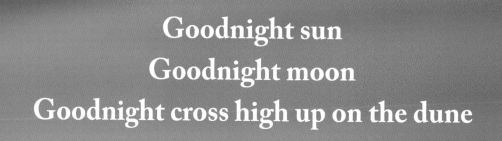

Goodnight sun
Goodnight moon
Goodnight cross high up on the dune

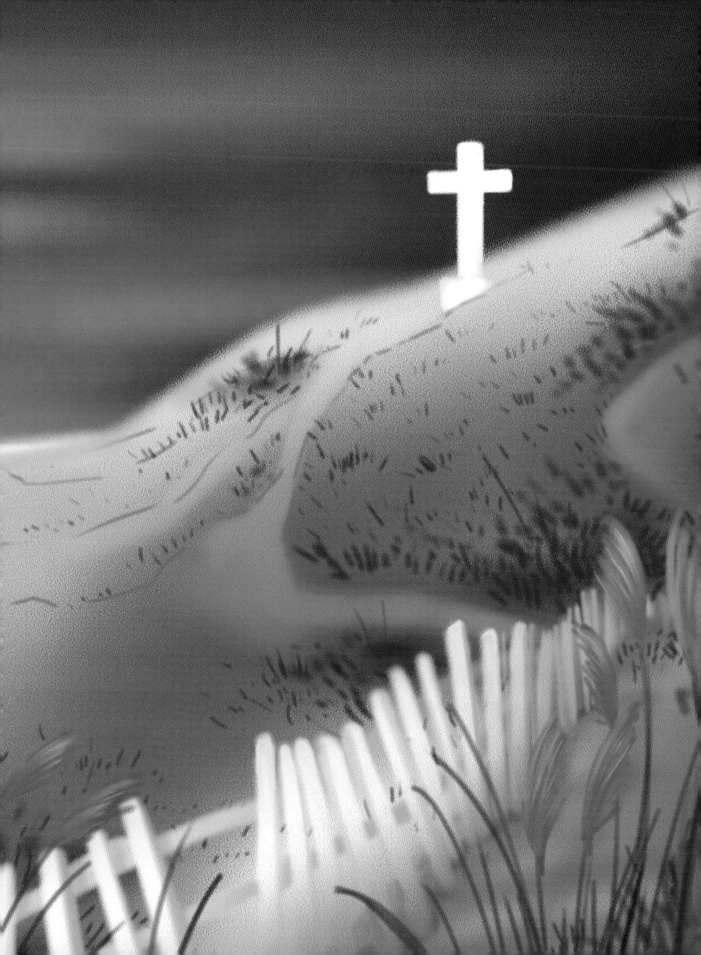

TURN
RIGHT
Pensacola
Beach

SCENIC DRIVE EAST ALONG
GULF OF MEXICO

MOTELS · RESTAURANTS

Goodnight sign and waters so blue

Goodnight beach ball with
a 360 degree view

Pensacola
Beach

Goodnight trestle
Goodnight trains up above

Goodnight drivers reading declarations of love

Goodnight Blue Angels with formations so tight

Goodnight Blue Wahoos with
fans cheering tonight

Goodnight surfers paddling all day

Goodnight boats cruising the bay

Goodnight Pier and fish swimming by

Goodnight lifeguards keeping watch from up high

Goodnight Fort Pickens
Goodnight to all

Goodnight to creatures big and small